come dive with me

BY RUTH BRADFORD

For JHLB

~ Never stop discovering ~

Come with me, the giant blue whale
Through the pacific, the Atlantic and Indian ocean I sail

I can swim 100 metres down to the depths below
To communicate with my pod my whale song echoes

The length of 3 buses my vast body glides
Barnacles cling to my skin, along for the ride

I open my mouth to scoop up millions of krill
Feeding for hours until I've had my fill

Travelling thousands of kilometres every year I migrate
From cold waters to warm to find a mate

The biggest animal on planet earth is the title I hold
If you spot a rare glimpse of me I'm a sight to behold

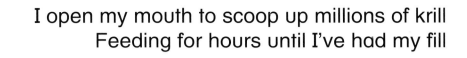

Come with me, the hammerhead shark
I hang out in deep water, where it can be quite dark

My strange mallet shaped head makes me easy to identify
But despite my reputation I'm really quite shy

Not just an odd shape, my head is full of sensors
Picking up electrical pulses from other creatures' defences

Big wide set eyes help scan the ocean for prey
My favourite meal to hunt is a tasty stingray

I don't lay eggs but give birth to live young
I have up to 50 pups at a time if I become a mum

Definitely one of the more unusual fish I could be
I won't be mistaken for any other shark you might see

Come with me, the hawksbill turtle
On my long migrations the world I encircle

I have 2 claws on each flipper and a distinctive beak
A solitary creature with my own company I keep

With beautiful patterns on my scalloped shell
In tropical shallow waters I like to dwell

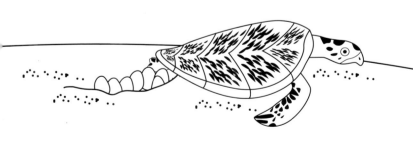

Females return to where they were born on the land
Making a new nest for their eggs in the sand

Hatchlings break free under the light of the moon
Across the beach to the sea they must make it soon

I've inhabited the seas for millions of years
Elusive I glide, crossing many frontiers

Come with me, the leafy sea dragon
I blend into surroundings with my foliage shaped pattern

Found only in waters around the coast of Australia
My intricate jointed plates ward off any predator

I'm ornately camouflaged to match the seaweed and kelp
Mainly drifting with the currents my small fins don't help

I look like a seahorse some people say
I use my snout like a straw to drink up my prey

Females deposit their eggs on the male dragon's tail
He's the one responsible for raising the young without fail

Fathers carry the eggs in a special brood patch
After 6 weeks then they're ready to hatch

Come with me, the lion's mane jellyfish
Meeting us in the wild is not something you'd wish

No other jellyfish can match our vast scale
My tentacles can grow longer than the size of a blue whale

I thrive in the freezing waters of the Arctic Ocean
Living in giant shoals we seem to float in slow motion

Made of 95% water our bodies are flowing
Our bioluminescence makes us look like we're glowing

With no brain, blood or nervous system, ghost like we appear
Each adult jellyfish only lives for a year

My 1200 tentacles can produce a sting quite deadly
But I mainly eat a fish, crustacean and fellow jellyfish medley

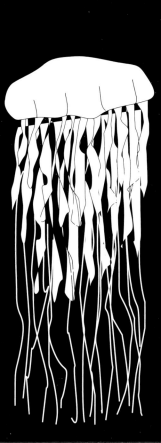

Come with me, the mimic octopus
As a master of camouflage to my surroundings I adjust

I have blue coloured blood and hearts numbering three
I like to hide out on the bed of the sea

I use my long arms to morph and change shape
To avoid any predators and help me escape

Mimicking lionfish, jellyfish, sea snakes and more
I can impersonate over 15 species found off the seashore

With skin that can change colour to alter my physique
And powerful jaws in a sharp pointed beak

With no bones in my body I can squeeze into tiny spaces
Waiting for my next meal I lurk with great patience

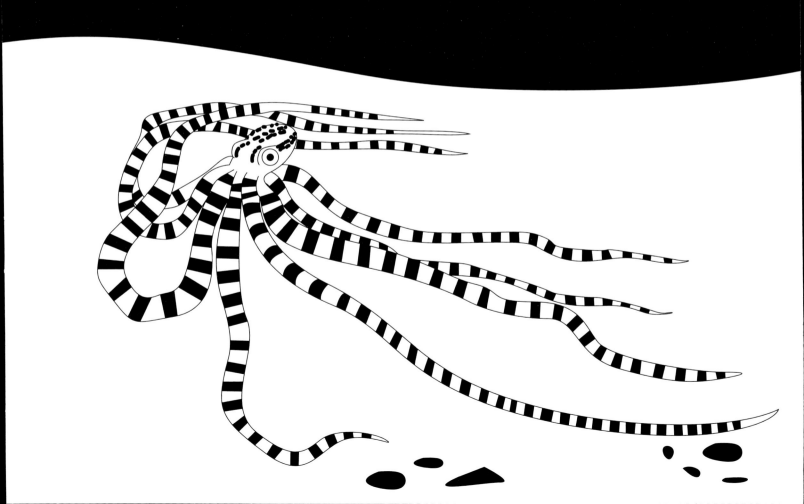

Come with me, the nudibranch family
Soft bodied molluscs we congregate quietly

No two are the same, with skin of all colours and patterns
More than 2000 known species throughout the world we are scattered

Our favourite habitats are the tropical shallows of the ocean
Residing mostly on sandy plains we seem to move in slow motion

What we munch on decides the colour we will be
Rinophore tentacles on my head help me find my next meal

Eating coral, sea sponges and even each other
Recycling toxins from prey to make poison for cover

When I emerge from my egg I have a shell to protect me
But as I grow into an adult I shed this and move freely

Come with me, the smooth head blobfish
I live 700 metres down in the pitch black abyss

With the title of the ugliest creature in the sea
I'm made to survive the water pressure bearing down on me

I don't move much and spend my days quite sedentary
I wait for food to pass by, I'm not much of an adversary

With no real skeleton or muscles to exercise
Just a partial backbone to hold me together lengthwise

When out of water my form becomes even uglier
My floppy face and wobbly skin looks so much funnier

Definitely one of the weirdest fish in the sea
But holding this title really doesn't bother me

Come dive with me, through the deep blue yonder
Full of amazing creatures that will fill you with wonder

Explore colourful reefs teeming with millions of species
Or float out in the open where there are creatures more beastly

From giants of the water like sharks and whales
To macro organisms like nudibranch and sea snails

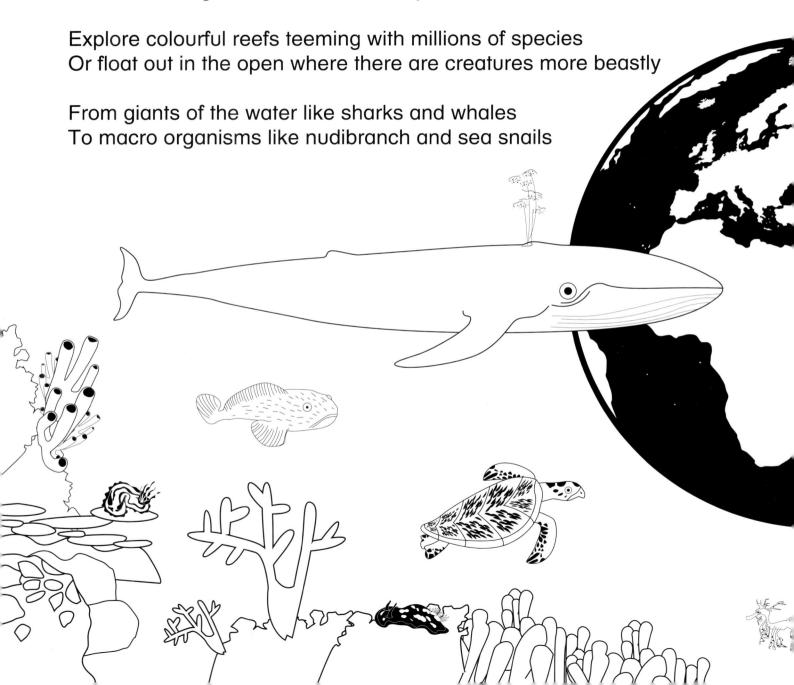

There's life at the surface and life on the sea floor
On coral, in trenches and on the seashore

Full of complex ecosystems that are truly organic
Covering over two thirds of the surface of our entire planet

So much about our oceans we have yet to uncover
So come with me and we can start to discover

where in
the world...

Greenland

Canada

USA

ATLANTIC OCEAN

PACIFIC OCEAN

South America